My First Time

Being Careful with
Strangers

Kate Petty, Lisa Kopper and Jim Pipe

Aladdin/Watts
London • Sydney

© Aladdin Books Ltd 2008

Designed and produced by

Aladdin Books Ltd
PO Box 53987
London SW15 2SF

First published in 2008

by Franklin Watts
338 Euston Road
London NW1 3BH

Franklin Watts Australia
Level 17/207 Kent Street
Sydney NSW 2000

All rights reserved
Printed in China

A catalogue record for
this book is available
from the British Library.

Dewey Classification:
363.1

ISBN 978 0 7496 8625 3

Franklin Watts is a division of Hachette Children's Books,
an Hachette Livre UK company.
www.hachettelivre.co.uk

Illustrator: Lisa Kopper

Photocredits: All photos from istockphoto.com.

About this book

New experiences can be scary for young children. This series will help them to understand situations they may find themselves in, by explaining in a friendly way what can happen.

This book can be used as a starting point for discussing issues. The questions in some of the boxes ask children about their own experiences.

The stories will also help children to master basic reading skills and learn new vocabulary.

It can help if you read the first sentence to children, and then encourage them to read the rest of the page or story. At the end, try looking through the book again to find where the words in the glossary are used.

Contents

Where's Mum? She always meets Sam after school.

Sam holds his teacher's hand. She will wait with him until Mum comes.

Who meets you after school?

4

Here's Mum. "Hello Sam!"
Mum is sorry for being late.
She's glad Sam's teacher looked after him.
Miss Smith never lets children go off alone.

Sam has seen that man at the gate before.
He doesn't know whose dad he is.

But what a beautiful puppy!
"Can we stroke the puppy, Mum?"

"You shouldn't trust a strange dog, Sam.
You can't tell what dogs or people are like
until you know them."

Mum and Sam go back to tell
Miss Smith about the man.

Who do you
feel safe with?

"Why can't I trust that man?"
asks Sam.

"Most grown-ups wouldn't
hurt a child. But you can't be
sure about strangers. Some
grown-ups can be bullies."

"Stay with those you feel safe with," says Mum.
"Like Miss Smith and Maria's mum," says Sam.
"Or Dad or Gran."

"Always tell one of us where you are going,"
says Mum.

The next day the man is there again.
At lunchtime Tina says, "I'm going to
ask that man if I can stroke the puppy."

Sam tries to stop her.

Tina knows she mustn't go
outside the gates.

What is she doing?

Tina really wants to stroke the puppy.
It looks so sweet.

But Tina wishes she wasn't on her own.
After all, she doesn't know the man.

Tina looks back to where all her friends are playing.

She decides to run back to the playground where she feels safe.

Where is a safe place to play?

Tina nearly knocks Miss Smith over.

"Come on, Tina. Let's go back into school."

The man with the puppy gets into his car.
He drives away quickly.

Tina is glad he has gone. She was right
to decide not to talk to the stranger.

Miss Smith talks to the children.

"People might pretend that your mum has sent them to pick you up. They might have other ways of tricking you."

Never take a lift from a stranger.

How can strangers trick you?

"It's best to go straight to someone you know."

"But you can stand up for yourself.
It's OK to say 'No' to a grown-up.
A caring grown-up won't mind at all."

17

When Mum collects Sam from school
the man isn't there.
"Tina wanted to stroke the puppy," says Sam.
"But she didn't trust the man and came back."

18

Sam says, "I wouldn't talk to a stranger. If he tried to make me go in his car I'd shout NO! I DON'T KNOW YOU! and walk away."

"That's right, Sam." says Mum.

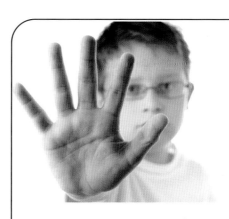

Don't talk to strangers!

19

At bedtime Mum hugs the children,
"So what have you learned today?"

"Don't go with strangers," says Jenny.
"Stay where you feel safe," says Sam.

Dad's home. "Can I have a hug?"

"Something happened today,
Dad," says Sam.
"Come on then, Sam. Tell me all
about it while I put you to bed."

21

waiting for Mum

asking
questions

telling the
teacher

22

deciding

feeling safe

saying
"NO"

Index

Find out more

Find out more about being careful with strangers at:

www.safekids.co.uk
www.juniorcitizen.org.uk/kids
www.thinkuknow.co.uk
www.childalert.co.uk

24